TWENTIETH CENTURY PARABLES

The stories Jesus told, in present-day settings,
for children

by

PATRICIA HUNT

illustrated by
NOEL WILLS
front cover by
MARTIN GREEN

© Printforce Limited

A catalogue record for this book is available
from the British Library   ISBN 0-948834714

Printed in Great Britain

CONTENTS

INTRODUCTION

One definition of a parable is 'an earthly story with a heavenly meaning', and there is a good deal of truth in that. A parable is a way of explaining something by putting things (illustrations in words) side by side.

The parables Jesus told are found in the Bible in the Gospels of St. Matthew, St. Mark and St. Luke. He took his stories from nature and from everyday life - normal, natural things which people see around them which would help understand the truths He was teaching. He used as illustrations such things as seeds, weeds, sheep, servants, coins, oil-lamps, and so on, all things with which His listeners would be very familiar.

Parables are easy to remember, which is one reason for using them as a method of teaching. People remember a story much more easily than they remember a lot of abstract teaching.

Sometimes Jesus explained the meaning of His parables, and sometimes He left His listeners to work it out for themselves. Not every detail in the parables has a meaning; mainly they are told to teach one important truth.

In this book the parables of Jesus have been re-written in modern language about modern people in today's situations. Thus it is hoped that young people will easily relate to them and understand the meaning behind them.

The original theme of the Biblical parables is also given, so that they can be compared with the 20th century ones. They are again written in modern language, but the Bible references are also given so that the original parables of Jesus may be read as they were first told.

MAKING THE MOST OF THIS BOOK

There are many things that children may do which will help to impress the stories in their minds.

1. Discussion and debates : The original and modern parables may be read in the group, followed by a general discussion. This might be started by asking a question such as: *'How would you have acted in such a situation?', 'Was the farmer/ shepherd/servant, etc. right to do as he did?';* and similarly with the characters in the modern parables. *'Would this story help people? If so, how?'* Can you suggest similar situations in which you (or other people) might find themselves today?

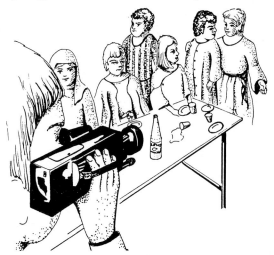

2. Acting : Acting the scenes of both original and modern parables can be a great help in getting the 'feel', and therefore the meaning of the story. One way of acting the original parables would be to go outside to some open space, field or hillside, dressed in costumes of the time (which are very simple to make) and to take slides of each scene, or even make a video. One Sunday School in Cheshire used the slides method very effectively, together with a taped version of the story (spoken by their own members) and were able to show the very creditable result to a much larger audience. This not only firmly fixed the parable in the children's minds, but it also gave a vivid presentation to many adults.

If this method is used, it is suggested that the original parable be read aloud, by a good clear reader, either before or after the acting so that the audience really understand what you are trying to portray.

3. Puppets : This could be a means of 'acting' for those who feel shy at putting themselves on the stage. Again a modern version of the Bible, such as the Good News Bible, could be used for a straight reading either before or after the puppetry.

4. Friezes and scrapbooks : Artistic youngsters might well make a frieze of the parables, scene by scene, which could be displayed in your meeting-place if space is available. Groups of children might take a parable each, and members of the group could each take on a separate scene, so that the whole tells the full story.

If the frieze idea is not practicable, the drawn scenes might be gathered together in a scrapbook, which need only be sheets of fairly strong paper stapled or stitched together with an attractive cover to form a book.

5. Play-writing : Older youngsters might like to write their own modern parables in the form of a play.

6. Practical action : Some of the parables might spark off some practical activity. For instance, *The Parable of the Talents* could be used in that each member of the group might be given a certain nominal sum of money, say £1; they should then be asked to use it to earn more money, the results of which might be given to a good cause of their choice. The original sum might be used to buy materials with which to make something which could be sold, and the resulting money could then be used to make more goods to sell again. A time limit should be given by which all moneys (plus the original sum) should be handed in.

The parable of the Mustard-seed might suggest the growing of a certain plant from seed - e.g. sunflowers - to see whose plant is the largest by a certain date. *The parable of the Good Samaritan* might suggest being on the look-out for someone to help or for some definite good deed to be done. *The parable of the Hidden Treasure* could result in young people being asked to give some object which they value (not simply something worn-out with which they have finished) to some good cause - e.g. the Salvation Army's toy or clothing collection. (n.b. It would be necessary to seek parents' permission before giving away clothing.)

Other ideas for this kind of activity may include: buying seeds to grow, and selling the resulting plants; buying sugar, flour, etc. and making biscuits to sell; buying shoe-cleaning or car-washing materials and volunteering to clean people's shoes/wash their cars for a certain charge; buying painting or colouring materials to make a picture to sell; buying model-making materials and making children's toys. The ideas are endless and youngsters will doubtless come up with many more - the more original the better - in fact a small bonus sum might be awarded for the most original way of using the initial sum of money.

There may well be other activities which may result from the hearing of a parable, and putting it into practical action is certainly one of the best ways of taking that parable to heart.

ROTTEN APPLES?
The Tares *(Matthew 13: 24-30, 36-43)*

The members of a Yorkshire village youth club had always got on very well together. They were almost hand-picked, for Jack Stones, their leader, did not encourage any but what he called 'the best type of young person' to join the club. They worked well as a team and won many of the local sporting and other events; they were even hoping that one day some of their best people might enter the Olympics - but that was looking rather far ahead!

It was a sad blow when the group heard that Jack Stones was leaving. 'Sorry, folks,' he said, ' but my job has moved to London and I've not much choice but to go. I'll miss you all, of course.'

'But who'll run the club?' asked the members.

'Fortunately, there is someone,' said Jack. 'There's a man called Bill Parks, who has just come to the village who is keen to help.'
'He won't be as good as you,' grumbled the more loyal but pessimistic of the members.

'Wait and see,' counselled Jack Stones.

Bill Parks duly arrived and seemed to be quite good. He even attracted several new members. The original 'gang' at first thought this was a good thing, until they found that some of the new members had little to contribute to the club.

'Half of them are useless,' complained Gareth, one of the originals. 'They're no good at sport, and some of them are rough types. One or two have even been on probation. We don't want that type here.'

Bill Parks said, 'But some come from poorer homes than yours and haven't been given a chance to train for anything. And I notice one or two have made friends with some of you folk, and that can only help both sides.'

'I still think we ought to turf them out,' said Gareth. 'Go on sir, tell them they can't stay unless they're going to help the club on.'

Bill Parks looked thoughtful. 'No,' he said, 'we must all be patient and see what happens; anyway, if we turned them out we might lose some of the other 'good' ones who have befriended them. It is wise to give them a chance and see how they turn out. We must all work together.'

Gareth and his friends gave up the attempt; they'd just have to wait and see if Mr. Parks was right.

Mr. Parks knew that in God's Kingdom there are good and bad, but it is not for us to judge between them. Only God can see the whole of a person's life and only He can judge.

WHO IS THE GREATEST?
The Pharisee and the Tax Collector *(Luke 18: 9-14)*

Louise and Mary both left school on the same day. They had been in the same form but had never been very friendly. Louise came from a well-to-do home and had always had everything she wanted; her indulgent father gave her any amount of pocket-money which, Louise thought, made her better than the rest of the form.

Mary, on the other hand, though clean and tidy and, in school uniform looking much the same as Louise, came from a poor home. Father was out of work much of the time, and her mother had a part-time cleaning job in a nearby office block. Nevertheless they were a very happy family, and with four children seemed to enjoy lots of simple fun.

Louise was very surprised when she found that Mary had been taken on for a trial period to work at the same offices where she herself had just started. 'Of course, I won't be here for long,' thought Louise, looking round rather disdainfully at her new colleagues. 'It's not really good enough for me; but as Mum says, it'll give me an idea of the humbler type of office job, and it's best to begin at the bottom. Mary, of course, won't get anything better than this for the rest of her life. She's not up to it, and she's lucky to have been taken on at all. I'm glad I'm not like the rest of this lot though; they all look so dull and ordinary. And I'm sure I can romp through this sort of work easily.'

She smiled a self-satisfied smile and began to tackle the work so fast and so self-confidently that she made a great many mistakes.

Mary, however, looked round rather nervously on her first day. 'I do hope I'll be able to cope,' she thought; 'but the others look friendly enough, so that if I get stuck I can always ask.' And she got on with her work slowly but thoroughly.

At the end of two weeks the Office Manager called both new girls in to see him separately. Louise went first thinking, 'He's sure to say, "We've never had anyone as good as you, although I know you made a few mistakes at first. That's only natural, but it is obvious you are too good for us here...".'

To her surprise, the Manager frowned and looked sternly at her and said, 'I'm afraid your work is very careless and you have made a lot of errors - even for a new girl. I hope it doesn't mean that you feel that you are too great, too important for this sort of work. But if you do not improve, I'm afraid I shall not be able to keep you on.'

Louise went out choking back the tears, but they were tears of shock and anger rather than tears of sorrow.

Mary was quite fearful at the thought of her intereview and began by saying to the office Manager, 'I'm so sorry, I ....'.

'What for?' said the Manager. 'I think you've done very well for a new girl. I know you made a few mistakes, but I also know that you were humble enough to ask for help so that you could put them right, and that you took care to see that they were corrected. I would like to keep you on and, if you continue like this, it won't be long before I can move you up to a higher position.'

THE ROVER'S RETURN
The Prodigal Son (Luke 15: 11-32)

Andy and Nick knew they'd get the family money when they were twenty-one. Their father was quite rich and had started a bank account for each of them when they were born. He was a hill-farmer and owned vast tracts of land in Northumbria.

'You know, that money would be useful *now* ,' said Nick. 'After all, I'm leaving school shortly, and I could go off and live my own life with it.'

'Not for me,' said Andy. 'I'd rather join Father and wait for my money until I'm twenty-one. I'll know a bit more about the world then, I hope, and meantime there's plenty of work to be done here.'

But Nick was impatient. He went to his father and said, 'May I have my share of the money now please? I want to make my own way in the world and I want to go to London where there'll be plenty of opportunities.'

His father was not very happy, but he wanted Nick to learn to stand on his own feet, and so, reluctantly, he gave him his share.

Off set Nick in joyful mood for London. He decided to go by train and to take a 1st Class ticket. 'Why not?' he thought. 'I've plenty of money now and I can travel in style if I wish to. I doubt if I'll ever need to work.'

On arrival in the capital he began spending his money, often foolishly. He'd never had so much before. He wasted a lot in gambling, always thinking it would make him richer - but it never did. He went to night clubs and gave or lent money freely to people whom he thought were his friends. He soon found that those who said they would pay him back easily forgot their promises, and his money was going far too quickly.

It was not long before Nick discovered he had no money left, and when his 'friends' found this out, they melted away. He was no more use to them. 'Fine friends they were,' thought Nick ruefully.

He seemed to know no-one in London now, whereas at home he would have known almost all the villagers. Alone and unhappy, Nick realised he must get a job or he would starve. It would be a big come-down from his life of the last few weeks, but what could he do? He was not trained for anything, and the only thing he knew a little about was farming - but no-one in London wanted a farmer. For the other sorts of unskilled jobs which were advertised, there were also plenty of applicants, and he stood little chance. No reasonable firm would take him on without references, and the hope of work seemed farther away each day.

Finally, after a long search, he managed to get a job sweeping the floors in a factory near the docks. At least it would enable him to buy a little food.

As he worked, he felt envious of even the lowliest workers there.

At least they had homes to go to, whereas Nick was sleeping rough. People who had known him in his 'rich' days sometimes passed the factory in their cars, but did not recognise the ragged-looking youth who was sweeping the floor. He couldn't have felt more miserable.

After a few weeks he made a big decision. 'I must swallow my pride,' he thought, and go back to my father and tell him how truly sorry I am. I'll offer to work as one of his staff - *if* he'll have me back - for even his newest worker is better off than I am.'

Full of determination, he left the factory and began the long trek home. No train this time - not even 2nd Class - for he couldn't afford it. He would have to walk, hitch-hiking where he could. It wasn't a very wise thing to do, but he doubted anyone would risk picking up a scruffy-looking character like him. To his surprise one or two kindly drivers did give him a lift, but he walked most of the way. Footsore and weary, he began to wonder what he could do if his father didn't have him back ...

He was getting within sight of home, at last, when he noticed a figure standing at the top of one of the hills. It was just by the 20-acre field, one of the most difficult to plough. Who was it, standing there just looking?

Suddenly the figure began to run towards Nick, and as he got nearer, Nick recognised his father! To his amazement, father rushed up to him hugged him and gave him a great welcome.

'Father,' began Nick, 'I'm sorry I've been so stupid. I ....'

But his father didn't seem to be listening. He turned to one of the farm-hands and said, 'Go back home, and ask my wife to prepare a big party. We shall have the best food and best clothes we can find for this great occasion. It is to be a day of great rejoicing.'

'Do you mean I'm forgiven?' said Nick, hardly able to believe this.

'Of course,' replied father. I have longed for your return ever since the day you left, and I have stood at the top of the 20-acre many times to see if I could see you returning. It has been a long wait, but I am so happy now.'

Meanwhile Andy had been working hard in the fields. He was a good farmer and his father was pleased with his work. Andy felt tired on his way home that evening, but was quickly alert when he heard sounds of music and revelry coming from the house. Whatever was happening? He called to one of the men and asked.

'Your brother has come home,' the man answered, ' and your father has ordered a huge party to be laid on, because he is so delighted to have Nick back safely. There'll be feasting and dancing all night, I expect.'

Instead of feeling happy, Andy was angry and refused to go indoors. His father came out and begged him to come in and join in the merry-making, but Andy said grumpily, 'Why should I? I've worked like a slave for you all these years and done all you ever asked me but you've never thrown a party for me. Now Nick comes home, having wasted all his money in London, I don't doubt, and you do all this for him. It's not fair!'

'Andy,' said his father gently, 'I know you're always here with me and you've always been a good worker; everything I have now will one day be yours, and I know you'll run the farm well. But we had to have a celebration, because we all thought Nick was dead - or at least that we'd never see him again. We never heard a word from him all those months. But now we know he is alive and has given up his bad and foolish ways. He's decided to come home and be sensible, and he really is truly sorry. So we must all rejoice at that. Come on in Andy and join in the festivities, so that we can give him a fresh start.'

NO ROOM FOR BAD HABITS
The Return of the Evil Spirit, (Matthew 12: 43-45 and Luke 11: 24-26)

Sarah had one really bad habit. She hardly ever told the truth. As she had a vivid imagination, she found it easy to invent stories about everything. Most people in the school said they never believed anything she said. She'd declare she'd done her homework, but it was soon discovered that she hadn't; whenever there was trouble in the class, Sarah always said loudly that it wasn't her fault and gave a long explanation of exactly what she was doing at the time, but quite often the trouble was eventually traced to her. Soon she found she was becoming very unpopular and had hardly any friends left.

One day, looking grimly determined, she told these few friends that she was going to take herself in hand. 'I know I've told lots of fibs,' she said, 'but I find it so easy to make up stories. But I'm not going to do it any more.'

17

'Good for you,' said her listeners. 'It will make a nice change to be able to believe you.'

When Sarah really decided to do something, she put her whole heart in it and did it with a will, and it wasn't long before the class and the staff were amazed at the new honest Sarah.

'Very refreshing,' they said, 'she really is a different girl.'

But Sarah's vivid imagination had to find something to work on. Soon she was inventing clever ways to take things from shops without paying, or ways in which she could get other people into trouble, without telling lies.

One day she went too far. Lucy, one of the younger girls, had tried to join in the older girls' hockey, and Sarah didn't want the child. 'Go on!' she stormed, 'we don't want kids like you upsetting our game. Anyway, you don't know how to play properly .' And she slapped the child, bruising her arm.

All this came to the ears of the Head who sent for Sarah to her study.

'Did you hurt Lucy, as her mother said?' asked Miss Hall.
Sarah was about to deny it, but she remembered her vow of honesty and said, 'Yes I did - but I didn't really mean to hurt her.'

Then, to the Head's surprise, Sarah burst into tears. 'Oh why can't I keep out of trouble?' she wailed. 'I've managed to stop telling lies, but now I seem to be in even more scrapes.'

'Sit down,' said Miss Hall gently, 'and I'll tell you.'

Sarah sat doubtfully, unsure of what Miss Hall was going to say.

'When you clear out something bad from your life,' began the

Head, 'it is most important that you put something good in its place. Otherwise, all sorts of other bad things, bad habits and so on, will come into your mind to fill its place. Now you're a determined sort of girl, and I'm sure that if you decided on some good habits, good things to do, you would find it much easier to get rid of the bad ones. You mustn't leave your mind empty. You've probably heard the saying "Nature abhors a vacuum"? And St. Paul told us to think about things which were good, and true and lovely. The sort of thing your mind thinks about is often the sort of person which you eventuallly become.'

Sarah raised her head and looked interested. 'Yes, I see,' she said. 'Well, for a start it might help if I could teach some of those little ones to play hockey properly, and I could make up my mind to do it kindly.'

'A very good start,' smiled Miss Hall, 'and don't forget that you were that age yourself once - not all those many years ago - and I'm sure you wouldn't have liked being bullied by a bigger girl!'

Sarah wiped her eyes, smiled 'Thank you, Miss Hall,' and set off to put her new vow into action.

CHANGE OF MIND
The Two Sons (Matthew 21: 28-32)

Tim and David lived with their parents in a small house in Coventry.

'They're good lads,' said their mother to their father one day.

'Huh, I don't know about that,' grinned father ruefully. 'They're not always obedient - either of them.'

'Well, they're learning and I think they are getting better,' mother said.

The next day was Saturday, and both mother and father had to go to a meeting in the city centre.

'Will you two be all right while we are away?' mother asked anxiously.

'Course we will,' said Tim robustly. 'We're not little kids any more,' added David. 'We *are* teenagers, don't forget.'

'Well, the Browns are next door if you need them,' said mother.

'Don't fuss,' said father, smiling. 'They'll be all right. Anway, I've got something for them to do while we are away.'

'What is it?' asked the boys together.

'I'd like you to make a start on clearing out the garden shed. There's quite a bit of stuff in there that's yours anyway, and you can take it to your rooms. Anything of your own that you no longer want can go in the dustbin. I want more space for gardening tools and materials for this summer. Will you do that for me?'

'I don't want to,' answered Tim, 'I'd much rather go and watch our team at football.'

'And I'd rather have a bit of help occasionally,' said father sadly.

'It's O.K., I'll do the shed,' said David.

'Good, thank you,' replied father. 'Come on, mother, it's time we were off.'

After their parents had gone, the boys looked at one another thoughtfully.

'I think I *will* go to the shed,' said Tim.

'But you said you wouldn't,' countered David.

'I know, but I've been thinking over what Dad said. He's right, we don't help him all that much. I'm going to start the clearing now.'

'You would,' grumbled David, 'just when I'd decided I wasn't going to bother.'

'But *you* said you would!' expostulated Tim.

'I know I did, but I'd forgotten about the football until you mentioned it, and now I've decided I'd rather go there. Surely I can change my mind?'

When their parents returned, Tim was still working in the shed, and quite enjoying it. He'd discovered some of his treasures which he'd previously forgotten. Of David there was no sign, and Tim explained about him having gone to the match.

'Well, I'd rather have it your way,' said father. 'It's far better to change your mind and do the right thing, as you did, than to promise you'll do something and then go off and do something else.

DO WHAT YOU CAN DO WELL
The Talents (Matthew 25: 14-30 and Luke 19: 11-27)

The class broke up, chattering volubly.

'It's all very well for you, Tom,' said Rob, 'You're good at things, you'll soon make money with your pound.'

'But I haven't decided yet what I'll do,' began Rob.

'Nor have I - yet,' put in Gary.

'I have,' said Gill. 'I'm not much good at brainy things, but I can cook, so I'm going to make buns and sell them, and then with the money I get, I'll buy more ingredients and make more. That ought to make the one pound grow into a lot.'

'I'm going to buy paper and colours and make pictures to sell,' said Sue.

'Oh well, you always were good at art,' sighed Tom, 'I'm hopeless.'

'I suppose I could make wooden toys for sale,' said Rob thoughtfully. 'Woodwork is about the only thing I can do, and I know I'm not brilliant at it ... but, I don't know. It'll be a lot of trouble and I don't have that much spare time.'

The class had each been given one pound at the beginning of Lent with instructions to use what talents they had to make the money grow.

'Some of you may not think you are very talented,' Mr. Smythe had said, 'but I know you can all do something, and I want you to use your talents well and to bring back the money you have made, plus the original pound, at Easter. That will give you six weeks and a bit of the Easter break.'

'What's going to happen to the money, sir?' asked Jeremy, who always wanted to know the details of everything.

'Good question,' said Mr. Smythe. 'Well, as I said, I shall want the pounds back, for they are only lent to you, but all the profits you have made will be given to the Save the Children Fund.'

'Does it matter *what* we do?' Sue asked.

'No, as long as it is legal and honest and doesn't hurt anyone else. In fact, I expect you'll all do something different; the point is that God has given us all different abilities and we can all do something. Now, off you go - and get working!'

The next day, Saturday, saw the majority of the class beginning their work in earnest. Gill had started her cooking with some very simple buns - she'd try more complicated ones when she had earned more money for extra ingredients. Sue began painting and had finished her first small picture that evening; her aunt would buy it, she hoped, perhaps for £2, but at least for £1.50.

Tom decided he'd garden for people. He bought a small trowel, which cost rather more than the £1, but his father paid the difference - provided I can have the money back from your first earnings,' he said, ' and then you won't have had an unfair advantage over the others.' Tom went out to several busy people and helped to keep their gardens weeded and tidy. He'd buy a small fork next, when he'd earned enough money, for that would help him get on more quickly.

Jeremy bought some shoe polish and cleaned the shoes of family, friends and neighbours at 15p per pair. It wasn't long before he had used up his polish and had to buy more - sometimes in different colours for different people.

After the Easter holidays, the class gathered round with their profits in their hands.

'What a variety of talents you have,' smiled Mr. Smythe ' cooking, painting, gardening, shoe-cleaning, car-washing (that was a profitable idea Gary, because your outlay for cleaning materials was very low) ...'

'Mostly water and a few rags,' grinned Gary, 'and I made £15!'

'Good,' went on Mr. Smythe, 'and Pam's baby sitting brought in £10; what did you use your pound for, Pam?'

'I bought a story-book, reduced at a book sale, to read to the children,' said Pam.

'Well, you read well and have a pleasant voice, and I know you are good with young children, so you used your talents well,' said Mr. Smythe.

'We've got £75 so far,' exulted Jeremy who had been counting the money as it had been handed in.

'He'll make a good accountant one day,' laughed Tom.

'And what about you, Rob?' asked Mr. Smyth. 'What did you do?'

Rob went rather red, 'Well sir, I didn't acutally do anything, but I kept your pound safe in my purse, and here it is.'

There was a surprised silence in the room. 'Why didn't you try to do something with it?'

'Because I'm no good at anything,' muttered Rob, 'I'm not clever like the others.'

'Now that's nonsense, you know,' said Mr. Smythe gently. 'Everybody can do something, it's just a question of finding out what it is and not giving up if you don't get it right first time.'

'He's not bad at woodwork, Sir,' put in Tom, 'In fact, I thought he was going to make some little toys.'

'I'm not that good - and I didn't like to try,' said the unhappy Rob.

'But you never will get good if you don't try,' reasoned Mr. Smyth. 'Our talents may often seem quite small to begin with, but God has given them to us for us to develop for the good of His Kingdom.'

'Well, all the other results will do that if they help Save the Children, won't they sir?' said Jeremy.

MAKE THE EFFORT

The Sower *(Matthew 13: 1-9, 18-23; Mark 4: 1-9, 13-20;*
and Luke 8: 4-8, 11-15)

'Shall we join?' asked Ann doubtfully. She was never one to make up her mind quickly and relied on her friends to chivvy her along.

'Dunno, really,' said Sue, 'it sounds O.K. but haven't we all got enough on - and exams coming up and all that?'

'I'd like to try it,' put in Gary. 'We've never been and those who do go seem to enjoy it; it'll be something new to do.'

'They all seem to put a lot into it,' said John, the realist. 'They meet once a week at least. But I'm game ... if some of you will come along too.'

'And we don't need to go again if we don't like it,' put in Ann.

The leader of the school's Christian Union, Mr. Clayton, was surprised and delighted when four new people turned up to his meeting that evening. Fifteen other young people turned to look at the friends as they entered.

They made Sue, Ann, Gary and John feel very welcome, and after refreshments, the business of the meeting began.

Mr. Clayton said, 'I'd better explain what we do. We're not goody-goodies - in fact most of us have to struggle hard to do what we think is right ...'

There was a chorus of 'I'll say!' and 'Don't we know it?'

'Yes, but what do you actually *do*?' asked John.

Sometimes we have a hymn or a chorus, but none of us is very musical, and we've no pianist, so it often sounds quite awful ...'

The group laughed, ruefully. 'You should hear us! All in different keys!'

'I can play a little .. ' ventured Sue.

'Splendid!' said Mr. Clayton. 'If you would, we'd all be so grateful, thank you so much. Now, to go on about what we do. We think how we can put our faith into action - for instance, Ned reads for the Talking Newspaper for the Blind, and Liz, who is good on a horse, regularly helps at the Riding for the Disabled Club; Jane shops on Saturdays for an old lady who can't get out.

We give a bit of our pocket-money each week for some good cause. It varies as we hear of needy things to help. And we all do our best to go to church each Sunday; some of us help there too."

All four friends enjoyed the meeting and decided to join.

Some weeks later, John found he was the only one of the four new ones at the meeting. Mr. Clayton was at a loss to understand what had happened to the others, and he kept an eye open for them in school. He came across Ann in the corridor and asked her what had happened.

'It's all too hard to understand,' complained Ann. 'The Bible and the church services, I mean. I'll just have to give it up - though I enjoy the group; they're a good crowd ...'

Mr. Clayton was sad. 'I feel you're giving up rather easily,' he said.

'But if I can't cope, it's a waste of my time,' protested Ann.

'No, I don't agree,' said Mr. Clayton. 'You usually have to put in some effort for the things that are worthwhile in life.'

Ann said, 'I'll think about it; but right now, I've got a swimming lesson. Sorry.' From her tone, Mr. Clayton felt it wasn't very likely she intended to come to any more meetings. She'd never been known for sticking to things for long. "Stickability" he called it, and he shook his head sadly and walked on.

Round the corner he almost collided with Gary. 'Sorry,' said Gary, 'I wasn't looking where I was going.'

'And I was wondering if we shall see you at the C.U. meeting tonight,' countered Mr. Clayton.

'Er - well - no,' said Gary, blushing. 'You see, all sorts of things have cropped up. We've a new dog at home and I take it out each evening. Then I got into trouble with my dad for staying out late at football, and I thought my faith would save me - and it didn't. I like the idea of C.U. though, it's a good thing.'

'But with you,' thought Mr. Clayton, 'it doesn't go deep enough; you haven't let it take root.'

The following morning Sue arrived at the school gates at the same moment as Mr. Clayton.

'Good morning Sue,' said Mr. Clayton. 'I've been wondering why we haven't seen you at our meetings lately? Apart from anything else, we've had to sing unaccompanied again, and our best friends could not say it was a lovely sound!'

'Oh yes, I'm sorry,' answered Sue, 'but you see, an aunt of mine died a while ago, and although I'm very sorry about it, she did leave me some money and I've been buying all sorts of new things - clothes, books, interesting things for all my hobbies. I'm afraid I just haven't had time to come to the C.U.' She smiled hopefully at him. 'You know how it is ...' She hurried off.

Yes, Mr. Clayton knew only too well how it was, and how easily people will give up something worthwhile for lesser, easier interests. Of the four newcomers, that left only John who was still coming regularly.

Mr. Clayton sighed, 'Well,' he thought, 'God's plan will always go forward while some of us believe, but how much faster things would move if only we all believed and acted as though we did.'

He saw John later that day. 'Hello sir,' said John. 'Can I bring a few more of my friends to our next meeting? I know at least two or three who would be interested.'

Mr. Clayton felt much cheered.

IS HE WORTH IT?

The Lost Sheep (Matthew 18: 10-14; Luke 15; 3-7)

The Junior Craft Club which met each week in the Church Hall was one of the most popular clubs in the neighbourhood. There must have been at least a hundred members, all aged between 8 and 12, and all enthusiastic to do all sorts of handicrafts as well as various team games and outdoor pursuits. Mr. and Mrs. Clarke, the leaders, encouraged every boy and girl to do the very best they could at anything they undertook. Some of the youngsters were

very clever and made wonderful things for sales of work, or for presents for their parents, or to give away to less fortunate children. Others joined in various games and played against other clubs in the district. Often they found they were surprised at what they could achieve when they really tried.

'My mum said she didn't know I had it in me,' said Debbie proudly after she had taken home a splendid shopping basket which she had made.

One day Mr. Clarke said, 'Where's Tommy Barrett? He hasn't been for two or three weeks.'

'He's not ill,' offered Tony. 'He lives near me and I've seen him about.'

'I think I know,' volunteered Richard, as he busily carved the funnel on a wooden engine he was making. 'He says he's not much good at crafts or games, so he's decided not to bother coming. He'd rather be out with the Sword Gang.'

'The Sword Gang? They're a rough lot,' said David, 'always getting into trouble. I bet his dad wouln't like it if he knew he was mixed up with them.'

'I shall go and look for him,' said Mr. Clarke, ' and if he's not at home, I shall go and search until I find him. I'll go now.'

There was an immediate chorus of protest -

'But it's dark Sir, and you said you'd help me with my picture.'

'And you promised we'd have a game on the computer. You did, Sir!'

'All of this I will do,' said Mr. Clarke, ' but I must find Tommy first; after all, he's one of the younger ones ..'

'Why do you want to bother going after him,' asked one of the girls. 'As he says, he's not much at handwork, and useless on most of the teams. We can get on as well without him.'

'Why bother, when you've got nearly a hundred who are keen?'

Mr. Clarke was deaf to all protests. 'I must go,' he said. 'Each one of you, however dull, however poor, is as important to me. I shall go and find Tommy and I will bring him back - or at least rescue him from any trouble he may be in.'

'He'll be in some sort of trouble, bound to be, if he's with that Sword lot,' said Tony.

'Is he really just as important as us, even if he is, well, thick?' asked David of Mrs. Clarke after Mr. Clarke had gone.

'Most certainly,' replied Mrs. Clarke. "Every human being is precious in God's sight, and it is wrong of us to despise anyone. After all, none of us is perfect.'

The Club worked on, thoughtfully.

Meanwhile, Mr. Clarke had found Tommy not at home, and his parents very worried when they learned he was not at the Craft Club. Mr. Clarke set off, looking in all the worst parts of the town and in the most unlikely places. After nearly two hours, he found Tommy, crouched in a dark alley crying bitterly. 'The Sword Gang threw me out,' he sobbed. 'They said I wasn't tough enough - and I was scared to come back to you. I didn't know what to do. Are you cross, Sir?' He wiped his tears on his sleeve.

'No, indeed,' said Mr. Clarke. 'I'm very happy that I've found you. It's too late to go back to the Club tonight - they'll all have gone home - so I'll take you back to your parents, and next Club meeting, we'll put on a bit of a party to celebrate your return!'

'I'll always come to the Club now,' said Tommy determinedly, 'even if I'm not much good. It's no fun mixing with rough boys like the Sword Gang.'

YOU NEVER CAN TELL
The Good Samaritan (Luke 10: 25-37)

Old Mrs. Black was toiling home to her cottage. She enjoyed walking to the village to shop, even though she was 75, and it was a pleasant area to live. The villagers were generally very friendly. Mrs. Black was not rich, not like all the newcomers who had moved into the village recently, but she manged. She would do her own shopping as long as she could, even though her rheumatism often made the walk slow and painful.

She had just reached the wooded bit, about halfway home, when there was a wild shout and a couple of youths set upon her, and took what money she had left and her brooch and ring. Laughingly, they ran off, while Mrs. Black sat down exhausted on a tree trunk to recover. She wished it wasn't such a lonely wood, as so few people passed this way. She tried struggling to her feet, but the effort was too great and her heart began thumping fiercely. Whatever should she do? It would be quite dark soon.

Presently a girl approached. She was about 18 and Mrs. Black tried to call to her, but couldn't raise her voice. The girl kept to the path glancing at the old lady as she passed. She thought, 'Poor thing, she must be having a rest; she doesn't look so good though. Still, I haven't time to stop. I must get home for a meal before the concert tonight. I don't want to miss that.' She gave Mrs. Black a brief smile and hurried on.

A little later a bright-looking boy from St. John's School came hurrying by. Surely he would help. St. John's was a good school; they taught them manners there. Her own son had gone there many years ago. Nervously, Mrs. Black tried to attract his attention. 'Er .. er .. son ..' but she was still so shaken that she could not get the words out.

The boy felt rather superior - wasn't he the brightest boy in his year? He took one look at Mrs. Black and wished these tramps didn't litter the place up so. This was a good wood, full of botanical specimens, and this old dear would probably leave all sorts of rubbish behind her when she left. But he'd been brought up to be polite, so he called out 'Good evening,' and walked on as far away from Mrs. Black as possible.

It was becoming darker now and Mrs. Black began to wonder what would happen. She didn't feel up to walking alone - and up that steep hill; she could easily trip up over a tree-root in the dark. Would it be possible to survive in the wood all night? She shuddered at the mere idea.

Suddenly, to her horror, she saw a very rough-looking youth approaching. He was untidy, and whistling jauntily. 'He'll be another attacker,' she thought, trembling, 'but I've nothing left to

35

take except my shopping.' She tried to get up to find somewhere deeper in the wood to hide. She was still so shaky that she had to sit down again before she fell. Would this nightmare never end?

The youth was coming straight towards her; he must have seen her when she moved. It was terrifying. Then, to her amazement, a gentle voice said, 'Hallo, Ma, are you all right? Can I help?'

Mrs. Black was so surprised that she burst into tears, and told him the whole sad story. Her wedding ring and that lovely pearl brooch! She couldn't replace those. 'Oh dear,' said the boy, putting a strong arm round her. 'If you can manage to get up with my help, I'll see you home. Where is it?' Mrs. Black told him, and asked, 'Who are you?'

'My name's Amarit and I come from Pakistan. I know what it's like to be set upon. Some of the lads at school are a bit tough and sometimes they get at me because I'm coloured and come from a poor home. There are seven of us kids and my dad's unemployed.'

'I'm so sorry,' said Mrs. Black. She was almost beginning to enjoy the walk now with Amarit's firm arm to help her up the hill.

'Here's my cottage,' she said at last. 'Come in and have a cup of tea and some cake; you've been so kind.'

'Thank you,' said Amarit. 'If you've got a phone, I'll ring the doctor for you. We'd better make sure there's no serious damage to you!' And he grinned a lovely broad grin.

'I don't know what I'd have done if you hadn't come by,' she said.

'Think nothing of it, ma'am,' said Amarit breezily. 'I'll be glad to pop in whenever I pass - just to see you're all right.'

THE GREAT PRIZE

*Hidden Treasure and The Pearl of Great Price (Matthew 13: 4
and Matthew 13: 45-46)*

Jeremy had always been a great collector. His mother called him a hoarder, because he never threw anything away.

'So long as you keep your stuff in your own room and don't clutter up the house with it, I won't object,' she said, 'but you must keep it tidy.'

And Jeremy did keep his treasures in his own room. His brothers said they didn't know how there was room for the bed, let alone space for Jeremy to sleep.

His main collection centred on railways. He had model engines of all shapes, sizes and ages, as well as an old Hornby track layout which had once belonged to his father. There was a small station with it, with signals, porters and people, and even a few little cars.

Jeremy collected cars too. He had over 30 model cars, some of them original Dinky models, which he knew would one day become quite valuable if he kept them in good condition. Jeremy did. He cleaned and polished his collection every Saturday morning, until his treasures shone like new.

One day, when Jeremy was going past the old school-room, he saw a notice about a sale of the contents of an old house, and today was the viewing day before the sale.

'Might as well have a quick look,' thought Jeremy, not very sure what was meant by 'memorabilia'. He wandered round and saw furniture and lots of old books and toys, some of them in poor condition. They had belonged to the old man who had once owned the house and who was now dead.

He was about to go out when he almost fell over a big cardboard box near the door. It was full of all sorts of things, and Jeremy got quite excited when he saw an engine wheel peeping out through the other bits and pieces. Carefully he lifted it out and found he was holding the most splendid green engine he had ever seen! Perfect in every detail too, even if it was a bit dusty.

'Excuse me,' he said to a man in a brown overall. 'Do you know how much this engine is likely to be at the sale?'

The man looked a bit surprised. 'Well I'm blessed!' he said. 'I didn't realise that was there. It shouldn't have been in a miscellaneous box like that. Actually, it's a very valuable antique, and will probably go for several hundred pounds. I'll put it somewhere special; it shouldn't be mixed up with junk.'

38

Jeremy handed it over with a sigh. How he would love to have it! But where could he get even a hundred pounds from, let alone several hundred? Then he had an idea. The man in the model shop down the road was always anxious to buy models from people. Jeremy knew him quite well. Suppose he offered the model-man his entire existing collection? Could he bear to part with them? He didn't know. All the way home he worried about it. Then he thought about the engine in the sale, and how he would love to clean it up. What a treasure it would be - especially if it really was an antique! He hardly slept that night.

The next day he had decided. He went down to the model-shop man with his list of all the models he already had, and he told the man about the green engine.

The man was delighted. He had originally sold Jeremy quite a few of his models, and moreover, he knew about the green engine. It really was a very valuable antique. Jeremy knew the model-man was honest and would not deceive him.

'I'd like very much to buy your present collection.' he told Jeremy. 'For how much?' asked the practical Jeremy.

'I'm willing to give you whatever the green engine costs,' he said, 'for I'll tell you, it was my grandfather who sold the green engine to the old man when he was young. So I know you're getting a genuine buy. In future years I don't think you'll regret it.'

Jeremy was delighted. Though he loved his collection dearly, he knew he'd be happy to sell them all in exchange for that one wonderful green engine in the sale. It was worth giving up lots of lesser things to have one really great treasure.

BE PREPARED
The Ten Virgins (Matthew 25: 1-13)

'I shan't be coming for a while now,' said Mrs. Main, who led the Youth Club.

'Oh, but you must!' chorused the shocked members. 'We're preparing for the fete and there are heaps of things to get ready. You said you'd help us.'

'Yes, I know,' said Mrs. Main, 'and I'd like to have done, but I have to go and look after my sick mother in Doncaster, and I don't know how long I shall need to be away. It may be weeks, or even longer. I just can't say when I'll return.' The club groaned.

'But I know you can manage. We've made a start on most things for the stall and we're fairly well on with rehearsing the play. It isn't as though you were little children. It will be a good opportunity to see how prepared you can be.'

The club members looked glum. 'Let's meet again next week, and sort out what's to be done,' suggested Susan, one of the brightest members.

They duly met and allotted various jobs to various people. Several of the boys were well into carpentry and several girls doing needlework and home-made biscuits and cakes, so there should be enough for the stalls. The food would go into freezers as the fete was several weeks away yet.

But not all the members were enthusiastic. 'We don't know when Mrs. Main will be back,' they said. 'The fete's weeks away yet; let's go out for a game on the green.'

'It's a lovely evening, much too nice to be indoors,' said Jock. 'I don't want to waste it working in here, and I can always work extra hard nearer the fete to catch up. I'm game to go out for a bit.'

So said several of the others, and about half the club members went off to play games outside. The same thing happened for the next three weeks, while those left worked harder than ever.

When they met the next week, they were amazed to see Mrs. Main there. 'My mother is much better,' she said. 'Let's see how you have all been getting on.'

Jock and his friends mumbled to the others, 'Can you lend us some of your work to show her?'

'There won't be enough to show what we've done too,' said Susan.

Mrs. Main was very sorry when she realised what had happened. 'You were not prepared,' she said to Jock and his friends. 'I said I didn't know when I should be back and you should have been ready. The fete is in less than two weeks now, and I fear that those who have not produced anything cannot take part.'

SMALL BEGINNINGS
The Mustard Seed (Matthew 13: 31-32; Mark 4: 30-32; Luke 13: 18-19)

It all began when Jimmy told a little lie. Somewhat to his surprise, everyone believed him when he said he hadn't been in the cloakroom where the money had been stolen from Tom's pocket. 'I didn't have a coat that day sir,' said Jimmy blandly, 'so I went straight home.' 'Right,' said Mr. Sanders, and went on to question the next boy.

It all seemed so easy to Jimmy, and he thought it was only a little lie, and as the money stolen was only 50p it really didn't matter. But in fact he had been in the cloakroom, though a little earlier in the day than the time Mr. Sanders was querying, and he had taken the 50p. It was spent now and Jimmy thought it could never be traced to him.

Having found that small lie easy to tell, Jimmy went on to tell bigger ones. His habit of not telling the truth just grew and grew. But he was found out in a good many of his lies, and it came to the point where no-one believed anything he said. It was odd too

42

that Jimmy never felt really happy inside about all this. Feeling a bit self-righteous, he burst out angrily in class one day, 'Why don't you believe me?'

Mr. Sanders said, 'Because we have so often found that you don't tell the truth. You were once an honest boy, but now your habit of lying has grown from small fibs until it is almost impossible to believe anything you say. We can't believe you, and it seems that from a small beginning a great evil has grown. If you don't mend your ways, you'll grow up into an untrustworthy, and very unhappy man.'

Jimmy began to look very miserable. He hadn't thought of it like that before. It took a great effort, but he stood up in front of the whole class and said, 'I'm sorry. I really will try and be more truthful; and, sir, I *did* steal Tom's 50p, though it was earlier than the time you asked us about.'

That speech was very hard to make, but strangely he felt happier now that he had admitted the theft. He wondered what punishment Mr. Sanders would give him, and he sat down feeling exhausted and hanging his head. There was a short silence, and when Jimmy looked up, he was amazed to see that Mr. Sanders was smiling.

'Well done, Jimmy,' he said. 'I'm not going to punish you this time, except to say that you must give Tom his 50p back - and anything else you have stolen from others.'

'Oh, I will, sir,' said Jimmy fervently, thinking he wouldn't have any pocket-money for himself for several weeks.

'And having made a small beginning to tell the truth, let's see if you can make *that* habit grow and grow, so that we see you becoming a dependable chap whom everybody trusts and likes.'

BE FAIR!
The Unmerciful Servant (Matthew 18: 21-35)

Judith's Uncle Andrew was sorting out his affairs before going abroad on a long business trip. He was a very kind man, but also rather strict - he liked everything done properly, and the children respected him and also loved him. As an uncle he was great fun.

He remembered that he had lent Judith £50 when she was saving up to buy a bike; which she could pay back gradually. But Judith had forgotten about it - she never seemed to have any spare pocket-money, and was always telling herself that she would repay Uncle Andrew a little *next* week. Being a busy man, it had slipped his memory, now he wanted to sort it out before he left.

So the next time he visited Judith's home, he took her on one side and asked her about the money. Judith had quite a shock, she had secretly been hoping that he had forgotten all about it. She looked very upset as she said unhappily, 'Oh, Uncle Andrew, I did mean to pay you back, really I did, but there seemed so many other things to do with my pocket-money that I never got round to it.'

'I know,' said Uncle Andrew, 'but I want you to learn the value of money, and I don't think you will if you get the idea that you can just borrow it and then forget to pay it back. That's just like stealing really, and the business world would never operate properly if it ran on lines like that.

'But I haven't the money,' implored Judith. 'Could you wait until you come back home? I should have saved up enough by then.'

'No, I won't do that,' said Uncle Andrew, while Judith looked near to tears. 'But I am prepared to forgive you the debt. We all have to learn to be forgiving as well as being honest about borrowing. Call it an extra birthday present, if you like.'

Judith's mood changed immediately. 'Oh uncle!' she said, giving him a hug, 'you are a brick! Thank you so much,' and she went out joyfully, thinking about money, and she met her friend Kate.

'Hey, Kate,' she said, 'do you remember that 10p I lent you last week? Well, I'd like it back - *now* - please.'

'Can't,' said Kate, 'I haven't any money until I get my pocket-money. I got a new video last week and it took all I had.'

Judith looked thunderous. 'Well, you've *got* to repay it. I want it now. I shan't be friends if you don't,' and she glared at Kate.

Furious, she didn't notice Uncle Andrew had come up behind her.

'What's all this?' he asked. 'I cancelled your debt to me - a large one - shouldn't you also be prepared to be generous to Kate, and at least give her time to pay back her debt to you?

PUT YOUR OWN HOUSE IN ORDER
Judging Others (Matthew 7: 1-5; Luke 6: 37-42)

Jane was a great one for noticing little details. If anyone around here did the slightest thing wrong, you could be sure Jane would notice it. 'I do like to have things right,' she would say, but some of her friends found this habit a bit trying.

'She's an awful know-all,' said Jenny one day. 'Why does she always pick holes in everything? It would be quite easy to catch *her* out sometimes, but she thinks she never makes any mistakes.'

'What about that time last week,' said Gill, 'when we found out she'd been lying to her mum about where she went on Tuesday evenings? We discovered she'd been telling her mum that she went to the library to look up things for her homework - '

'She *is* a bit of a swot.' put in Jenny.

'Yes, but we know she never went near the library; she spent the time with that group of trouble makers.'

'My mum won't let me mix with them,' said Jenny, ' because she says they're a bad influence.'

Just then Jane herself came up. 'Hullo,' she said breezily. 'Oh, by the way, Gill, your library book's a day overdue; I've just noticed it on your desk. You shouldn't keep it out past the date, you know, because someone else might want it.'

Gill did not reply.

'Oh, and Liz,' went on Jane, 'I do think you ought to remember to water your plants more regularly. I noticed the one on your bedroom window-sill as I came past your house this morning; it was wilting badly. It's not right to neglect them like that.'

Jenny took her courage in both hands. 'You know, Jane,' she began, 'even though we're friends, and we do have fun together ... we do think you should remember your own wrongs as well. I mean, we all know you don't go to the library on Tuesday, as your mother thinks you do, so you must have been fibbing to her for ages. We know where you do go and your mother wouldn't like it, nor would your father.'

Jane had gone very red in the face.

'Perhaps when you've put your own problems to rights, then will be the time to come and sort out ours,' added Liz.

Without a word Jane walked away, obviously thinking hard, but her friends had very little trouble with her after that. Gill even bumped into her in the library on the next Tuesday evening.

47

TOO LATE TO MAKE AMENDS
The Rich Man and Lazarus (Luke 16: 19-31)

The wealthiest boy in the school ws undoubtedly David. He lived in a big house, with its own swimming-pool, and his father had several cars, including a Daimler, in which David was sometimes driven to school. He seemed to have an endless supply of pocket money and was never short of anything. But in spite of all this, some of the boys noticed that David never seemed really happy, and was often rather mean with his possessions.

'I'd always be happy if I had his money,' remarked Alan one day.

'I wish he'd share some of it with us,' said Jake. 'I'm going to ask him for a bit of his cash. We could do a lot with a few extra pounds, and I'm sure David would never even miss it.'

'Don't be stupid,' said Ian, but Jake ignored him. Jake came from a poor home and his mother worked hard in a factory to help to earn enough to feed and clothe Jake and his six brothers and sisters. But even so, they seemed a happy family and were always having fun together.

A few weeks later the boys were shocked to read in the paper that there had been a business crash in the city and that David's father had lost all his money. They could hardly believe it.

'My dad says David's father is having to sell all his cars - even the Daimler,' said Richard who lived quite near to David.

'I believe he's got a lot of debts to pay off too,' said James, 'though how a man as rich as him can ever be in debt, I can't understand. Perhaps they'll have to leave that big house?'

'Maybe it isn't as bad as we think,' said another boy optimistically.

But they decided things must be even worse when, a few days later, David arrived at school on a bicycle. He confirmed the disaster to his only real friend, Alex.

'My parents say I can't have any money until all this business is sorted out - and it may take *ages*. I wonder if some of the boys would give me 20 pence each; at least I'd be able to buy a few crisps and a drink of coke or something.'

'Well, I'll help,' said Alex loyally, 'but I don't think you can expect much of the rest. I mean, when you were rich, you had your chance to help some of them but you didn't do it, did you?'

'No,' agreed David, looking more miserable than ever. 'I never thought about it. I just felt I was O.K., and they could look after themselves. I won't be so selfish in future.'

BE FORGIVING
The Two Debtors (Luke 7: 36-50)

There had been great excitement in the school when Simon's home was burgled one night. Simon was quite a hero and gave everybody details of all that the burglar had taken - everything of value, it seemed. 'Jewellery, money, the TV set,' said Simon, 'all my cassettes and videos, and he even had the nerve to drive off in dad's car. I feel really rotten about it.'

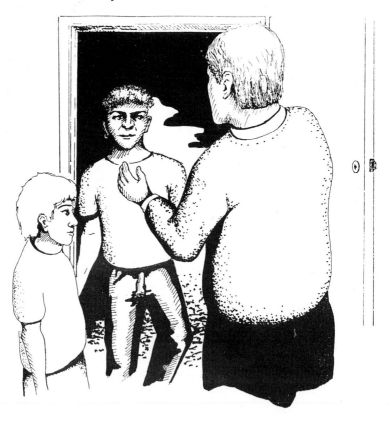

'Never mind,' said his friend Graham, trying to cheer Simon up. 'Come and have a game of conkers.'

When Graham won that game, Simon felt even more miserable. Nothing was going right for him. Graham was a generous friend and he said, 'Don't worry, we'll forget it. I know you're upset. You can have all your conkers back.'

'At least I've got one friend,' thought Simon.

A few weeks later, the burglar was traced, caught and duly sent to jail. It was proved he had been responsible for several burglaries in the area, and many stolen goods were found at his home, and returned to their owners.

Interest lapsed for several months until it was reported that the burglar's term of imprisonment had ended and he was now free.

'He'll never do any good now,' said one of the older boys. 'That sort doesn't change.'

'Well, if he steals again,' said a girl, 'what good has prison done him?"

'What would you do if you met him in the street?' someone else asked. 'You'd recognise him from the pictures in the papers.'

'I'd bash him if I saw him,' said a belligerent 10-year-old.

'I'd run fast in the opposite direction,' said one of the girls. 'What would you do, Simon? You're the one most affected.'

'I don't know,' said Simon slowly. 'Perhaps we'll never see him.'
But when he got home that night, he put the question to his father.

'Well, I certainly shall see him,' said his father, 'because I'm going to invite him round for a meal.

Simon gasped, 'Oh dad - you *can't*.'

'But I must,' said his father. 'If someone doesn't give him a chance, he never will get any better.

The school's verdict when they heard about it was generally, 'Well, don't invite us on the same day, Simon!'

Simon felt rather nervous on the day the burglar was to come. He looked at the man narrowly, and decided that he had tried to rise to the occasion by putting on his best suit. He seemed very quiet during the meal, until suddenly he turned to Simon's father and burst out, 'I don't know how you can do this. I mean, can you really forgive me for what I did? I really am very sorry and I'd like to make a fresh start, but nobody has ever treated me like this before. I've no family or friends, and it's hard on your own.'

'But I forgive you,' said father, 'and I'll do what I can to help you make a fresh start.'

The man could hardly keep back his tears of joy. 'Thank you, thank you,' he said. 'You don't know how much it means to me to be treated like that. It'll be much easier if I know someone is expecting better things of me.'

Afterwards, Simon's mother said to her husband, 'Do you think he really will go straight now?'

'I think it's much more likely than it was before we talked to him, because if you have been forgiven and know that someone respects, and even loves you, you will be more likely to want to love in return. If you've been forgiven much, you will love much.' He smiled. 'Not like Simon and that conker match. Graham "forgave" him, I think because he saw Simon was depressed, but that was only a little thing by comparison.'

'Yes,' said mother, 'but I think even that gesture has increased Simon's respect for Graham.'

FIRM FOUNDATIONS
The House on the Rock *(Matthew 7: 24-27; Luke 6: 46-49)*

It was a lovely seaside holiday that year. Mary and her younger brother Chris and sister Emma always enjoyed coming to Sandhill-by-the-sea, and Chris and Emma, who were 5-year-old twins could not remember going anywhere else and thought Sandhill was 'the best place in the whole world.' Mary, who was eleven, enjoyed it too, but felt she was a bit too old for the sort of games which the twins played.

However, she did have a new hobby of collecting shells and making decorated boxes from them; so while the twins enjoyed their buckets and spades, Mary spent her time searching for pretty shells.

On the day before they were due to go back home, the twins

decided they were each going to build a sand-castle.

'Mine will be the most beautiful sand-castle ever,' declared Emma, 'and to make it look extra special, I'm going to find some shells like Mary does and stick them all over it.'

'I shan't do that. That's silly,' said Christopher robustly. 'Who ever heard of a pretty castle? Mine's going to be a strong and mighty castle that nothing can move - and when we come again next year, it'll still be here.'

The family laughed. 'I'm afraid that won't happen,' said mother. 'What about the sea and the waves and the tides? They will wash it away.'

'And strong winds will blow it down - they do blow sand, you know, especially if we have as windy a winter as last year,' put in Mary.

'And think of all the people who will come on the beach before next year,' added father, 'they're bound to wear it away.'

Poor Chris looked very crestfallen. He couldn't doubt the logic of all this, but he had never been one to give in easily.

'Well,' he said slowly, 'It'll last till - till tomorrow.'

'It just might,' said father. 'It's early in the year and there aren't many people about - but it will really depend on just where you build it.'

'I know where I'm going to build mine,' said Emma. 'Just there,' and she pointed to a beautifully smooth patch of sand, very flat and far enough back for the sea not to be able to reach - she hoped! It certainly looked to be a splendid site for a castle.

Chris hadn't thought about the site and he began looking round for somewhere really suitable. He too saw the wisdom of building far back from where the waves might reach, and at last he spotted what he thought was the right place.

'Mine's going to be high,' he said, 'so the people inside can be on the lookout for enemies coming from far off. It's going to be on top of that big boulder there!' and he pointed to a rocky site nearer to the sea wall.

'But there's not much sand there, hardly any in fact,' cautioned Mary. 'You'll have a long way to carry your bucket.'

'Doesn't matter,' said Chris, to whom bucket-carrying was one of the happiest jobs in life, 'it's a better site.'

'It will certainly get some shelter from the sea-wall and from the jetty,' said father. 'Off you two go and start while mum and I have a rest in these deck-chairs, and I suppose Mary will go looking for more shells.'

So the Great Castle-Building Operation began. Emma got on the faster, because her site was ready to start on and there was lots of good sand nearby. Chris had harder work, because first he had to build up a flat area on top of the boulder so that the castle would stand straight, and then he had to lug his buckets from the sand to the rocks.

It took them all afternoon, but by tea-time there were two splendid castles proudly displayed. Emma's was prettily decorated with shells of all kinds and swags of sea-weed, while Chris's had turrets and ramparts and even a flag flying from the highest point. How proud the builders were!'

'Well done, both of you,' said the family, 'you've worked very hard.'

Next day the twins' first request was .... 'Can we go down to the beach and see our castles before we go home?'

'Well, we've time for a quick look at the beach, but the castles probably won't be there, you know. It was quite breezy last night.' Said mother.

'Let's make sure,' said Chris determinedly, and off they went.

Emma rushed straight to her site only to find - no castle. The waves had reached that far and, together with the wind, had demolished her building. All she could find were a few of her shells. She hastened to pick these up and look for more, 'because I'm going to make boxes like Mary. At least they won't fall down!' Emma believed in making the best of a bad job.

Chris's castle, high upon its strong boulder, hadn't been touched by the tide, and the jetty had sheltered it from the wind, but the flag had vanished and the castle itself did not look as perfect as it had done yesterday.

'Never mind,' said Chris triumphantly. 'It's still *there!*'

'That's largely because it had a good firm foundation,' said father. 'Emma's castle looked equally good, but sadly, it was only built on sand.'

OPEN TO ALL
The Net *(Matthew 13: 47-50)*

'Let's have a party,' said Anne at the Youth Club one day. 'We haven't done anything really special for ages.'

'True,' said John, 'and after all, we did win the Sports Shield, so we have got something to celebrate.'

'How about making it a sort of recruiting drive and inviting new people to come and join us?' suggested James.

'That's a good idea,' agreed Penny. 'We could do with some new members.'

'Well, the hall is big enough to take lots more,' added Lucy, 'we don't use even half of it most nights, except when we're playing badminton.'

So they asked Stephen, their group leader and he gave permission. 'But how are you going to get in the new people?' he asked.

'Easy,' said Anne, the optimist. 'James is very artistic, so he can design us a poster to put on the notice-board outside, and we can also send separate invitations to folk whom we know and who might come.'

'You'd better ask people to let you know if they intend coming,' said Stephen, 'or you could find yourselves in a mess with the catering.'

The poster duly went up on the board, with instructions that people wishing to come should let Anne know by a certain date. The invitations also had R.S.V.P. on them. She turned up at the Youth Club about a week after the closing date with a long list of acceptances.

'There are millions of them!' she exaggerated. 'Well, not far off a hundred.'

'Let's look at their names,' said John. 'We might know some of them.' ·

'I think you'll find we know quite a lot,' said Anne darkly.

Together they went through the list.

'Well, we don't want *him*,' began James, 'nor *him*, nor *her*. They're not the right sort for our Club.'

'And we're certainly not having those dreadful girls from Wellington Street,' said Anne. 'Six of them - and they're *awful*!'

'There's at least another six here whom I wouldn't have at any price,' said John. 'A bad lot, they are. What a rotten list!'

'I'd rather not mix with those two at the bottom of the page,' said Lucy; 'they're not my type at all.'

'Well, that's cut down the list a bit,' said John.

'But, can we?' said Anne thoughtfully. 'We didn't put down any conditions for accepting, did we?'

Unnoticed by any of them, Stephen had walked in during this conversation. He looked round the group and said, 'Anne is right. She asked, "Can we?", and the answer is "No". It is not up to us who can come at this stage. We put out a general invitation and so we must accept those who want to come. None of us knows how they'll turn out, and it isn't right for us to reject them before we know them properly. Some of them may well fit in a lot better than we may think. If they decide they want to become full members, then we'll have to see if they are willing to abide by the rules of the Club. But at this stage, judgment is wrong. We must learn to be welcoming to everybody - without grumbling!'

YOU WON'T KNOW WHAT YOU'RE MISSING
The Wedding Feast (Luke 14: 15-24)

'A Bazaar Party' said the invitations. 'Whatever's that?' people asked.

It was certainly unusual and it turned out to be the specially different way in which Gary was proposing to celebrate his 18th birthday. Until about a year ago, Gary and his family had lived in Ethiopia. They had seen terrible famines, children starving, babies dying, and all manner of sickness and disease, much of it caused through the people not having access to clean water.

Gary's father had been working there as a doctor, and his mother had been helping as a nurse in the makeshift hospital. But all the good work they were doing seemed as a drop in the ocean, compared with the needs of the people and the enormous amount of work there was to do. The facilities were dreadful too - non-existent in most cases. The hospital building was roofed with a mixture of thatch and corrugated iron, and often the roofs leaked or sometimes collapsed altogether.

Gary used to help where he could; he was quite a handyman when he tried, and being reasonably fit, he thought he should do what he could to help the many who were suffering.

During his six years out there, he had made friends with some of the Ethiopians, and had found them hard-working people, determined to make the best of things, in spite of their poverty.

It was all this which had given Gary his idea for such an unusual party.

'I want people to come and enjoy themselves and have a good time,' he said, 'but I also want them to bring something for the Bazaar for Ethiopia, which we will be having the day after.'

'What sort of things do you have in mind?' asked his father.

'They can bring things to sell on one of the stalls, or they can make something to sell, or they can offer to organise a game, or just give some money, or do anything else they can think of which will help Ethiopia. In fact, their contributions, in whatever form they wish, will be the passports to the party. No help, no party!'

'It's a good idea,' said father. 'I just hope people will come when they find there are strings attached,as you might say. Anyway, it will be a challenge.'

Gary sent out lots of invitations, and was quite disappointed when he got more than a few negative replies.

'I don't mind the party bit,' said some, 'but the thought of helping at a bazaar is a bit off-putting. I don't know what I could do.'

('Feeble,' said Gary in private disgust.)

'I would come,' said another, ' but I've just passed my driving test, and I simply must go out and practise.'

'I've got a new girl-friend,' said one of Gary's best friends, 'and we're going walking in Derbyshire that day, otherwise we'd love to come.'

'I must do my garden,' said another, 'the grass is about a foot high.'

Gary was very cross about these replies. 'They're just making excuses because they don't really want to help,' he said. 'Well, they won't come to my party now. I shall go out and find people whom I hadn't invited and ask if they'll come.'

This he did and still there was room at his party for more. So he went out again, inviting people he hardly knew at all, until at last all the places were filled.

The party was an enormous success, and the results of the bazaar the next day exceeded all expectations. Many of the people Gary had hardly known turned out to have all sorts of unexpected skills and talents which were a great help. He made many new friends who wanted to know whether they could help in any other ways. Altogether it was a wonderfully exciting venture.

And Gary's original friends who hadn't come? When they heard about it, they wished they had accepted and had joined in the fun.

THERE'S MORE TO LIFE THAN MONEY
The Rich Fool (Luke 12: 13-21)

Old Miss Smith who kept the village shop was known to the children as 'Old Grumpy' - and grumpy she certainly was, for she seldom had a smile for anyone. Her sole aim in life was to make money. Not that she over-charged or cheated her customers in any way, for she was strictly just and honest to the last penny; but she was greedy, and her thoughts were always on what she would gain.

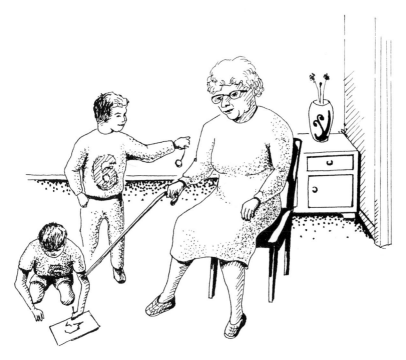

As her shop was the only one in the village, she found making money was quite easy, for unless they went out of town, there was nowhere else near enough to shop. And her produce was always good and reliable, so most people shopped there anyway, rather than bothering to take a journey to the nearest market-town.

Miss Smith had hardly any friends, for she was always too busy counting up her money to have time for them.

'Don't you ever go out?' asked Mr. Hall, whose house was nearest to her shop.

'Goodness me, no,' replied Miss Smith, shocked, 'and leave all my wealth here? Burglars might get in while I was away and steal my treasures.'

'What treasures?' asked Mr. Hall.

'The ones I buy with my money. I have many priceless antiques and pictures here.'

'Then why don't you invite people in so that they may enjoy your treasures with you?' suggested Mr. Hall reasonably?

Miss Smith was affronted. 'Certainly not!' she snapped. 'Suppose they wanted some of them. And what do I want with friends anyway?'

Mr. Hall went out thinking deeply. 'I can see why she has no friends,' he thought, she thinks more of her money and her treasures than she does of people.'

So each night Miss Smith sat counting her money and gloating over her treasures; and if anyone dared to call after the shop was closed, she refused to answer the door.

One morning, on their way to school, the children saw workmen at the side of the shop. 'She's having builders in,' said Robert, Mr. Hall's son. 'Dad says she's having an extension built, because she hasn't got enough space for all her stuff.'

'Then she ought to have,' said Alan, 'That big place - and only her in it! Disgusting!'

The extension grew and soon it was almost as big as the shop itself. Old Grumpy could sometimes be seen standing in the doorway of her shop and gloating over it. It was almost finished when one night there was a terrible fire - and the shop and the extension were burnt to the ground.

The fireman rescued Old Grumpy, blackened with smoke and looking crosser than ever - but not hurt.

'My treasures! My treasures! My money!' she wailed. 'All gone! Whatever shall I do and where shall I go?'

Robert's mother was a kindly soul and she invited Miss Smith to her house.

'We've Robert and two younger children - toddlers,' she said, 'but at least it will be a roof over your head until you can sort yourself out, and we can feed you with the family.'

'What! Old Grumpy living here? Mum, you *can't!*' said Robert in disgust when he heard.

Mrs. Hall replied, 'Now, I know you don't like her, but this is a time when you must be kind; remember she is an old lady and she has had a very bad shock.'

'I'll try,' sighed Robert resignedly, but he knew all his school-friends would feel sorry for him.

When Old Grumpy had been with the Halls for two or three days, they began to see another side of her. She let Robert show her his books and toys and really seemed interested in his games; despite her rheumatism, she even got down on the floor and played with the toddlers.

After the children had gone to bed one night, she said to Mr. and Mrs. Hall, 'You know, that fire has really taught me something. Since I've been living here I've discovered that there are other joys in life besides money. I've found joy in people - and it has made me far happier than my money ever did, even though I thought I was happy when I was getting rich. I'm not going to let wealth be my aim in life in future.'

'That's wise,' said Mrs. Hall gently. 'Getting things and money just for yourself never has been the road to happiness ...'

'But getting to know you and playing with the children has been the most tremendous fun,' grinned Mrs. Smith, grumpy no more.

THE GENEROUS EMPLOYER
The Labourers in the Vineyard (Matthew 20: 1-16)

The most popular man in the village was undoubtedly Farmer Appledore. His rosy cheeks and infectious grin made him a favourite with everybody, especially the children. He was kind and generous and spent so much time telling stories to the younger children that people wondered how ever he had time to run his fruit farm.

Passing children were often given an apple or a pear on their way to or from school. 'Doesn't it take all your profits?' a neighbour asked.

'Not a bit,' grinned Farmer Appledore, 'and if it does, who's counting? I'm not after every penny I can get, and you know, I just love children.'

'But you've a family of your own?'

'Aye, six of them, but there's always room for others. I've got lots of young friends, aged from about two to seventeen. Keeps me young!' and his rosy face creased in a happy smile.

One Saturday morning, Farmer Appledore found that due to illness, no less than ten of his farm-hands had not reported for work. 'My! What shall I do?' he thought. 'At my buisiest time too, and there are all the fruit-berries need picking today, acres of them. I know, I'll ask some of my young friends if they'd like to help me.'

Word soon got round the village, and within half-an-hour five or six young folk aged between eight and twelve had volunteered to help with the fruit-picking.

'Now you can eat as much fruit as you wish,' he said. (My guess is that you'll soon get tired of that!') and at the end of the day I shall pay you each one pound.'

The youngsters set to with a will, but were obviously not as fast as the experienced men would have been; so Farmer Apledore went out looking for more help.

'Would you like to come and help pick soft fruit?' he asked some more youngsters. 'I will pay you at the end of the day,' and so more hands came to help on the farm.

In the early afternoon he went out again and found others who agreed to help. It was almost tea-time when he came across a group of boys standing idly on the green.

'What are you doing?' he asked.

'Nothing. Nothing to do,' was the reply.

'Would you like to come and give a hand with picking soft fruit?' he asked.

They too agreed and came to join the other young folk at work.

At the end of the day, Farmer Appledore called all his new workers together and gave each one a pound coin. On seeing this, those who had come early and had worked all day, grumbled aloud.

'That's not fair,' they said, 'we've been working all day, and some of these have only done about an hour's work, and you've paid us all the same. We should get more.'

'Did I not agree to pay you £1,' said the farmer. 'If I want to give others the same, then surely that is my business. You must not be jealous and grudge my kindness. Am I not allowed to do as I like with my own money? You mustn't think you're greater than others who have worked too.'

'There's some Coke in the kitchen, if you'd all like a drink before you go home!

APPENDIX

THE ORIGINAL PARABLES

THE ORIGINAL PARABLES

The Tares *(Matthew 13: 24-30, 36-43)*
Jesus told this story as a way of showing what the kingdom of heaven is like:

One day a man sowed his field with good wheat seed. While he was asleep, an enemy came and sowed weeds (tares) among the good seed. No-one knew about this until the plants began to grow. Then the man's servants noticed what had happened and asked their master what they should do.

'Shall we go and pull up the weeds?' they asked. 'No,' replied the man, 'because if you do so now, you might easily pull up some of the good seed with the tares. Let the field stay as it is until the harvest; then I will tell the harvest workers first to pull up the weeds and burn them, and then to gather the good wheat and store it in my barn.'

When the disciples (Jesus' friends) came and asked him what this parable meant, He said: 'The man who had the field is the Son of Man (Himself) and the field represents the world. The good seeds are the people who follow the right way (God's way) while the weeds are those who follow Satan (the Devil); he is the one who sowed the weeds. The harvest is the end of the world, and those who gather it are the angels. So at the end of the world, Christ will separate the good and the bad; it is not for us to separate them now.

The Pharisee and the Publican (or Tax-Collector)
(Luke 18: 9-14)
Jesus told this parable to people who felt that they were always in the right and who looked down on others:

Two men went up to the Temple to pray; one of them was a Pharisee and the other was a publican (or tax-collector). [The Pharisees were a group of people who believed it was better to obey every tiny detail of the law rather than to keep the greater law of love to all. Jesus taught the way of love, but the Pharisees had not understood.]

When the two men arrived at the Temple, the Pharisee stood apart by himself and said, 'I thank God that I'm not like everyone else, greedy, dishonest and evil. I fast twice a week and I give one tenth of my money to You, God.' He felt very superior to the tax-collector.

But the tax-collector stood back with his head down and simply said, 'God, have mercy on me, for I am a sinner.'

Jesus said it was the tax-collector who had the right attitude to God, not the Pharisee; and He ended, 'Everyone who thinks himself great will be brought down, and those who think themselves humble will be made great.'

The Prodigal Son *(Luke 15: 11-32)*

When the Pharisees and scribes were grumbling because Jesus received sinners and even ate with them, He told them this story, to prove He loves even the worst of us.

A man had two sons, who would inherit his wealth after he had died. One day, the younger son came to him and asked, 'Can I have my share of the property now?' The father decided to give his son his share and the son left home and went to a far country.

There he wasted and spent all his money in foolish ways until there was none left. Then a bad famine spread through the country, and the lad was left without food, money or a home. He decided he would have to take a job, and eventually found one on a farm looking after the pigs. He felt very miserable and hungry, for no-one had given him anything to eat; he would gladly have eaten even the pigs' food.

At last, he realised how stupid he had been and he thought, 'Even my father's servants have enough to eat and more, and I am starving. I must swallow my pride and go back home and tell father I know now how sinful I have been. I will ask him if he will take me on as a hired servant, for I know I am no longer fit to be called a son.' So, feeling very contrite, he got up and began the long trudge back home.

He was still a long way off, but getting in sight of home, when his father saw him and came running towards him. He threw his arms round the boy and kissed him.
'Father,' began the son, 'I'm sorry. I've sinned against God and against you, and I know I'm not fit to be called your son ...'

But his father didn't seem to be listening. He cut short his son's apologies and said to the servants, 'Bring out the best robe for my son, and a ring for his finger and shoes for his feet. Bring the prize calf and we'll have a great feast to celebrate his return! For we all thought he must be dead - but he's alive! We thought him lost - but now he is found!' An so the party began.

Meanwhile the elder son had been working in the field. On his way home, he heard the sound of music and dancing, and he asked one of the servants what it was all about.

'It's your brother,' said the servant, 'He has come back home. Your father is having a party.'

At this, the elder brother was filled with jealous anger and refused to go into the house. His father came out to beg him to come in.

'No,' said the elder son, 'All this time I've worked for you and obeyed you, and you've never given a party for me.'

'My son,' said the father kindly, 'I know you're always here, and everything I have now will be yours, but we are rejoicing because your brother was lost and is now found. It is right to make merry and be glad about this.'

The Return of the Evil Spirit *(Matthew 12: 43-45; Luke 11: 24-26)*

Jesus said: When an evil spirit (meaning the thoughts, words and deeds of wickedness and wrong) leaves someone, it looks around for another place to go. If it cannot find anywhere, it decides to go back from whence it came. If it then finds its original home swept clean and empty and in order, it then goes and finds seven other evil spirits more wicked than itself; so the person in whom it had first lived is in a worse state than when he began.

It has been said that nature abhors a vacuum. When we get rid of something bad in ourselves, we must replace it with something good.

The Two Sons *(Matthew 21: 28-32)*
Jesus was teaching in the Temple one day and the priests and elders (leaders in the Church) were asking questions about authority. So Jesus told them this parable:

There was a man who had two sons and he asked both if they would go and work in the vineyard that day. (The vineyard was where the grapevines grew.)

The elder son said, 'I don't want to,' but later on he changed his mind and went and did the work his father wished.

The younger son's reply to the question was, 'Yes, I'll go,' but he did not do so.

Jesus asked, 'Which one of the sons did as his father wished?'

Jesus's listeners replied, 'The elder one.'

Jesus said that the outcasts and people who were often despised would go into the Kingdom ahead of other people, because once they had seen the right way to live, they had believed and obeyed. But the other people, who thought themselves in the right and respectable, when they saw the right way to live, had not repented and believed.

The Talents *(Matthew 25: 14-30; Luke 19: 11-27)*
Here is another parable which Jesus told to explain what the
kingdom of heaven was like:

A man was preparing to go on a journey, and so he called his
servants together and put them in charge of his affairs while he
was away. He gave each one some of his money, according to
how he thought they would be able to deal with it. To one man he
gave 5,000 silver coins, to another 2,000 and to another 1,000,
and he expected them to use the money wisely during his absence.

The servant who had been given 5,000 coins went away and
invested the money so that, before long, it had doubled its value
and had earned another 5,000 coins. The servant who had been
given the 2,000 coins to look after used them to earn another
2,000 coins. But the servant who had received the 1,000 coins
was very angry about it and thought his master was a hard man.
He was fearful and decided the only thing which he could do with
the money was to bury it in the ground.

After a long time, the master came back home and asked his
servants to report to him how they had fared during his absence.
He was delighted to hear the first two servants say that they had
doubled the amounts which their master had left in their care.
'Well done!' he said to them. 'You have been faithful with what
was entrusted to you, so I will put you in charge of greater
amounts. Come and share in my joy!'

When the servant who had receive the 1,000 coins came forward
he had no increase to show. He had made no use of the money,
but had buried it in the ground; so all he could give his master
was the original 1,000 coins.

'You lazy servant!' said the master. 'Why did you not at least put
the money in the bank where it would have earned some interest,
instead of burying it in the ground? He took the money from him

and gave it to the servant who had had the 5,000 coins.

God has given us all different talents and abilities, according to how He thinks we can make use of them. He expects us to use them to the very best of our ability, whether they are small or great, many or few.

The Sower *(Matthew 13: 1-9, 18-23; Mark 4: 1-9, 13-20; Luke 8: 4-8, 11-15)*
One day, by the sea-shore, crowds gathered round Jesus, as they so often did. In order to be able to talk to them, he got into a boat and pushed it out a little way from the shore, and spoke to the people who were standing on the beach. He told them a story about a sower who was sowing his seed by hand; this was the usual method in those days before there was any machinery to do the job.

The sower was casting his seed on to the land, but it did not all go where he intended it. Some fell on the pathway and was eaten by the birds. Some fell on to rocky ground, where there was not much soil, and because it could not grow deep enough roots, the sun scorched the little plants and they withered away. Yet more seed fell into the thorn bushes, where the thorns soon choked the young plants, so they did not grow either. But some of the seed fell on good ground, as the sower had intended, and it grew splendidly and multiplied itself into a really good crop.

When the disciples asked Jesus to explain what the story meant, He said: The seed is God's Word, and the types of ground are the hearts of the people who hear it. That falling on the path is like someone hearing God's Word and not understanding it, and Satan comes and snatches it away from him. That falling on rocky ground is like someone who hears God's Word and receives it joyfully at first, but it doesn't go deeply into the mind and take root; so when troubles come along because of it, he immediately gives up believing in it. That falling into the thorn bushes is like someone hearing God's Word, but who lets the worries and problems of life and the love of money and other things choke the message so that it cannot grow.

The seed falling on good soil is like those who hear God's Word and let it grow deeply in their hearts, so that they understand it. Then it will grow and increase and multiply many times over.
It has been said that the parable might be better called 'The Parable of the Seed' rather than of The Sower, because it is so much more about the Seed (God's Word) than about the Sower (God Himself).

The Lost Sheep *(Matthew 18: 10-14; Luke 15: 3-7)* and **The Lost Coin** *(Luke 15: 8-10)*
Jesus told this parable to show how important to God are the 'little' ones. Even today some people think that children are of no importance to the Church until they are grown up; Jesus said that was not so. Each one is supremely important to Him. Jesus said:

There was a man who owned one hundred sheep, and one day he discovered that one of his sheep was missing. He did not say, 'I have 99 other sheep; why should I bother with just one?' No, he left the others safely grazing and went out and searched until at last he found the sheep which had strayed.

He was full of joy and happiness, and picked up the stray and carried it back home. Then he called together all his friends and neighbours and said, 'Come and celebrate with me, for I am so happy that I have found my lost sheep!'

Jesus ended the story by saying that there was more joy in heaven when one sinner repented and came back to God's right ways than over 99 respectable who did not need to repent.

Jesus also told a similar story about a lady who had 10 silver coins. (In those days the coins were often worn on a band round the head.) She lit a lamp and searched and swept in all the dark corners of the house until at last her coin was found. She too rejoiced with her friends and neighbours over the return of the coin.

This story had the same message and meaning as 'The Lost Sheep'.

The Good Samaritan *(Luke 10: 25-37)*

One day, a teacher of the Law asked Jesus, 'What do I have to do to have eternal life?' Jesus replied by asking the man, 'What does it say in the Scriptures?' and the man answered, 'Love God with all your heart, soul, strength and mind, and also love your neighbour as you love yourself.' 'That is right,' said Jesus, 'if you do that then you will gain eternal life.'

But the lawyer wanted to show that he didn't ask questions as apparently simple as that, so he went on to ask, 'But whom do you mean by my neighbour?' Once again, Jesus told a memorable story to explain it:

A man was walking one day from Jerusalem to Jericho. The road was lonely and desolate, and went through rocky country for about 10 miles or roughly 16 km. Suddenly the man was attacked by a band of robbers who took all that he had, beat him up and left him lying by the roadway half dead.

After a while a priest came along the road. When he saw the man lying there he did not stop, but walked by on the other side. Later a Levite (a helper in the Temple) came by and he looked at the man but, again, did not stop.

The third person to come along was a Samaritan - one whom the Jews regarded as untouchables. The wounded man must have felt there would be no help there, for the Jews and the Samaritans had been deadly enemies for a very long time.

However, the Samaritan was a good man and he felt very sorry when he saw the victim and he went over to see what he could do. He tended the man's wounds, bound them up, and then helped the man up on to his own beast and took him to an inn where he might be cared for.

On the following day he gave the inn-keeper two silver coins and said, Please take care of the man and, if you have to spend any more money, I will pay you back the next time I come along this way.'

Jesus ended by asking the lawyer, 'Which of these three men acted like a real neighbour to that wounded man?'

'The Samaritan who acted kindly towards him, ' replied the lawyer.

'Then you go and behave in the same way,' answered Jesus.

A true neighbour is someone who gives help wherever it is needed, not only to people he likes, but to anyone, regardless of who he may be. It may be anyone we meet at school, at work or at play. It is easy to do good to those you like; not so easy to be kind to people who you think are your enemies.

Hidden Treasure and **The Pearl of Great Price** *(Matthew 13: 44-46)*

In these two short parables Jesus gives us pictures of what the kingdom of heaven is like:

(a) It is like a man who one day comes across some treasure hidden in a field. He hides it again and is so delighted at what he has found that he goes and sells everything he has so that he may buy the field with the treasure in it.

(b) It is also like a merchant who was always on the lookout for fine and beautiful pearls. One day he came across the finest one he has ever seen. It was quite unusual and of such great value that the merchant went and sold all that he had previously owned in order to go and buy that pearl.

To live God's way and to gain His kingdom is worth giving up everything else in life.

The Ten Virgins (or The Ten Girls) *(Matthew 25: 1-13)*
This story is about being prepared. It tells of a wedding. In those days in Palestine, there was no fixed time set for a wedding, and the bridegroom came to collect his bride whenever he chose, accompanied by his friends. It was usually after sunset and the friends would bring their lamps with them to light the way. So the ten girls of this story had to be ready with their oil-lamps.

Jesus said that five of the girls were wise and had extra flasks of oil ready, but five were foolish and did not take any extra oil. Unexpectedly, one night, they heard the cry, 'The bridegroom is here! Come and meet him!'

The five foolish girls hadn't sufficient oil and they asked the other girls if they may borrow some of theirs. 'No, we cannot do that.' replied the wise girls, 'for if we do, there may not be enough for both you and us. You will have to go and buy some for yourselves.'

So the foolish girls went to buy oil. While they were away, the bridegroom arrived and off the procession set to the place where the feast was to be held. When the foolish girls returned later, they found they had no claim to be guests, and they were not allowed in to the wedding-supper.

Many people are not prepared for Jesus when He comes. Today He comes to us through the lives we live, the people we meet and the things which happen to us - but often we are not prepared and do not recognise Him. Being prepared in this way is something which we all have to do for ourselves. We cannot rely on others and hope to 'borrow' from them.

The Mustard Seed *(Matthew 13: 31-32; Mark 4: 30-32; Luke 13: 18-19)* and **The Yeast (or Leaven)** *(Matthew 13: 33; Luke 13: 20-21)*

This is another of Jesus' parables about the kingdom of heaven. This one shows how it grows from small beginnings.

Jesus looked around and said to the people, 'The kingdom of heaven is like a tiny grain of mustard seed, the smallest of all seeds. When it is planted, it grows and becomes a huge tree, putting out big branches so that the birds can come and build their nests in its shade.

The second parable is somewhat similar. It tells of a woman making bread into which she puts yeast (or leaven) with the flour. There, invisibly, it works away until the whole of the dough swells, rises and so increases in size.

So in life, small things, small beginnings, can grow into much bigger things - be they good or bad. The Church (the beginnings of the kingdom of God as started by Jesus) began with only twelve men (the apostles); they preached and taught and spread the good news of God to others, who in turn told others, until the Church now has millions of members throughout the world. So the kingdom of God goes on increasing, and Christians today do all they can to help the Good News to go on spreading.

The Unmerciful Servant *(Matthew 18: 21-35)*

One day Peter, Jesus' leading apostle, asked how many times he
ought to forgive someone who had wronged him. 'Seven times?'
suggested Peter. 'No,' Jesus replied, 'not seven times, but seventy
times seven.' In other words, we must go on forgiving. Then he
told this parable:

A king once decided to check up on his accounts, and as he
started one of his servants was brought in who owed the king a
vast sum of money, over a million pounds. The man simply could
not pay and so the king ordered that he and his family should be
sold as slaves in order to pay the debt.

'No, no,' implored the servant, going down on his knees. 'Just be
patient, and I will pay you all I owe.'

The king was a merciful man and he felt sorry for the man. 'All
right,' he said, 'I will forgive you the debt.'

Very relieved, the man went out, and he came upon one of his
colleagues who owed him a small sum of just a few pounds. He
grabbed the man by the throat and cried, 'You pay me what you
owe me!'

The second servant could not do so, and he begged the first man
to be patient and his few pounds would be paid.

But the first servant would have none of this, and he mercilessly
had his debtor cast into prison until he could pay.

When the other servants saw what had happened, they felt it to be
very unfair and went and told the king what had happened.

The king was angry and summoned the first servant to him again.

'You wicked man!' he cried out. 'I forgave you your huge debt because you implored me. Should you not also have been equally kind and merciful to your colleague, who owed you only a very little? You will now be put in jail yourself until you have repaid all that you owe.'

Jesus said that we must forgive others if we want God our heavenly Father to forgive us.

Motes and Beams (Judging Others) *(Matthew 7: 1-5; Luke 6: 37-42)*

Jesus gave several little illustrations to warn us not to judge other people harshly when we forget that we all have sins enough of our own. Sometimes he put the message in a humorous way which would make His listeners smile and remember.

He said, 'Why do you bother about trying to take a tiny speck (a mote) out of someone else's eye, when there is a great log (beam) sticking out of your own eye? If you first took the log out of your own eye, then you would be able to see more clearly the speck which is in your brother's eye - (i.e. someone else's).

He also said, 'How can one blind man lead another blind man? If he tries, both of them will fall into the ditch.'

It is hypocritical to judge or to try and lead others when you are far from perfect yourself.

We must treat others as we would wish to be treated ourselves, for the way we treat others is the way in which God will treat us. So we must not judge and condemn; we must forgive and give generously. Then God will reward and give to us in far greater measure than we have ever given to anyone else.

The Rich Man and Lazarus *(Luke 16: 19-31)*

Jesus told this story to show that we must respond to the message in the Bible, and also to show how much wealth can make people blind to the needs of others:

There was once a very rich man, who was clothed in beautiful clothing and who ate well and lived in great luxury. At his gate there lay a poor man named Lazarus, who was covered with sores which the dogs came and licked, and who hoped he might get just a few crumbs which fell from the rich man's table.

Eventually Lazarus died and was taken by the angels to heaven. The rich man died too and went to Hades (hell) where he was in great pain and torment. Somehow, he could see at a great distance the great Old Testament leader Abraham, with Lazarus at his side.

'Father Abraham,' cried out the rich man, 'have pity on me! Send Lazarus to dip his finger in water that he might cool my tongue, for this fire causes me great agony.' But Abraham replied, 'Do you remember, when you were on earth, how you had all the good things in life while Lazarus had only the bad things? But now your roles are reversed and there is a great gulf between you which cannot be crossed.'

'Then,' said the rich man, 'will you send Lazarus to my home where I have five brothers, so that they can be warned, and at least they will not suffer as I am doing?' Abraham replied, 'But they have Moses and all the prophets to warn them; why can't they listen to what they say?'

'That would not be enough,' said the rich man; 'but if someone were to go back to them from the dead, then they would surely take notice.' Abraham answered, 'If they won't listen to Moses and the prophets in the scriptures, then they won't be convinced if someone were to return from the dead.'

The Two Debtors *(Luke 7: 36-50)*

One day a Pharisee named Simon invited Jesus to come and have a meal at his house. People did not sit at chairs at the table, as we do, but reclined on couches round a low table, and when Jesus arrived, Simon did not show Him any of the ordinary courtesies of the day, such as offering to wash his feet.

During the meal, a woman who had led a bad life, came in and stood behind Jesus, weeping. She had with her an alabaster jar of ointment, and as her tears fell on Jesus's feet, she wiped them with her hair, kissed them and anointed them with the ointment.

When Simon the Pharisee saw it, he thought to himself, 'If this man Jesus were really a prophet, He would know what sort of a woman this is and how sinful a life she has led.'

Jesus knew what Simon was thinking so He told him this story:

'There was a certain money-lender to whom two men both owed money. One owed him 500 coins and the other owed him fifty. Neither of them had the money to pay, and the money-lender forgave them both their debts. Which one of them do you think would love the man most?'

Simon answered, 'The one who had been forgiven the most.'

'That is so,' said Jesus, and turning to the woman, He said to Simon, 'You see this woman? When I arrived at your house, you did not offer me water to wash my feet, nor greet me with a kiss. But she has washed my feet with her tears, dried them with her hair, kissed them and annointed them with ointment. Her many sins are forgiven, for she has shown great love; but he who has been forgiven little only shows a little love.'

To the woman He said, 'Your sins are forgiven; your faith has saved you; go in peace.'

The House on the Rock *(Matthew 7: 24-27; Luke 6: 46-49)*

During one of His teaching sessions, Jesus was explaining how important it was to live in His way (God's way).

He said that everyone who listened to His words and obeyed them was like a wise man who built his house on a rock, digging deep so that it could be set on a solid foundation. Then when the rains came lashing down and the floods swirled around and the winds roared about the house, it would not fall down, because its foundations were on solid, immoveable rock.

On the other hand, everyone who did not obey Jesus' words was like a foolish man who built his house on sand. Then when the rains came lashing down and the floods swirled and the winds roared about the house, it would fall down with a mighty crash, because its foundations were so insecure.

All buildings need firm and strong foundations in order to withstand any storms or other troubles which may arise.

The rock represents Christ Himself and His teaching, which is the only foundation for a good, strong, spiritual life. So a person's character, built on faith in Christ and obedience to Him, will be stable against the storms and troubles of life.

By contrast, the sand made a very shifting, unstable foundation, as did the teachings of false prophets and the following of other gods than Christ.

The way we build our life is our own choice, but Christ clearly showed which is the right way.

The Net *(Matthew 13: 47-50)*

This is another parable which Jesus told to help His listeners understand the kingdom of heaven.

He said the kingdom was like a fishing net thrown into the sea, which caught all kinds of fish. The net He was speaking of was not the ordinary small net such as fishermen might use today for fishing in a river or lake. It was a very long net which was used near the shore. The bottom edge was weighted down with weights, probably of lead, while the upper edge, supported with corks, floated along the surface of the sea. It was sometimes called a drag-net.

When it was dragged along the sea and on to the shore, it was found to contain many varieties of fish from the area which had been swept, for escape from it was well-nigh impossible.

The fishermen drew it ashore and the fish were sorted; the good ones were collected in buckets or vessels, while the bad ones were thrown away.

The net represents the Church (not the building, but the body of believers) and the fishermen are the apostles and their successors (including Christians today) who, by spreading God's Word, gather into the Church all kinds of people. 'Then,' said Jesus, 'the angels at the end of the age will separate the evil from the righteous.'

The Wedding Feast *(Luke 14: 15-24)*
One day, when Jesus was dining at the house of one of the rulers who belonged to the Pharisees, He told this story:

There was once a man who gave a great banquet to which he invited many people. When everything was ready, he sent one of his servants to tell people that the time was ready for those who had been invited to come.

But one after another, the guests began to make excuses, for they all felt that they had better things to do. One said, 'I cannot come, because I have just bought a field and I need to go and see it.' Another said, 'Please apologise for me too, because I've got five new pairs of oxen, and I must go and try them out.' A third said, 'I'm afraid I can't come. You see, I've just got married, so please excuse me.'

All these excuses meant that the guests did not really want to come to the banquet. The servant went back and reported to his master as he had been told. The master was angry with all these excuses, and he said to his servant, 'Go out into the streets and lanes of the town, and bring in the poor, the crippled, the blind and the lame.'

The servant did so and came back and said to his master, 'Sir, I have done as asked, but there is still room at the banquet.'

'Go out again, further,' said the master, 'into the countryside and, using your greatest efforts of persuasion, urge people, press people to come, so that my house will be full. For none of those who were invited will partake of my feast.'

The meaning of the parable is this:

The man who gave the banquet is God, and His servant is Jesus. The first people invited are those whom one might expect to be invited. When they refused, the outcasts and despised people were invited. They gladly obeyed, but still there was room, because God invites all mankind to His kingdom. Then the servant (Jesus) goes further afield and invites those who were not Jews (i.e. Gentiles) to come, for His kingdom is not limited to any one race, and none should feel they are superior to the others.

The Rich Fool *(Luke 12: 13-21)*
Once when Jesus was asked to sort out a family quarrel about an inheritance of an estate, He declined to do so, but told this story:

A rich man had a great deal of very fertile land which yielded abundant crops. He harvested so much grain that it became more than he could cope with.

'What shall I do?' the man wondered, 'I haven't enough space to store all my crops properly.'

Then he had an idea. 'I know what I'll do. I'll pull down all my present barns and in their place I'll build bigger ones, so that then I'll have plenty of space to store all the grain and my other goods too. I'm a lucky man with all these good things stored up like that; they'll last me for many years. I will be able to take life easy, to eat, drink and thoroughly enjoy myself.'

But God said to him, 'You are very foolish, for this very night you will die, and then what will happen to all these things you have been hoarding?'

Jesus ended the story saying, 'This is what happens to people who pile up riches for themselves, but who do not see that the best treasures are those which are lasting in God's sight.'

The important things in life do not depend on how many possessions or what great riches we have. In fact riches can be a hindrance to happiness, and a happy life can result even if one is comparatively poor, providing we approach it in the right way - generously, thankfully, unselfishly loving God and our fellow men.

The Labourers in the Vineyard *(Matthew 20: 1-16)*
This parable follows a discussion which Jesus was having with His apostles about entering the kingdom of God. Peter had asked, 'What shall we have? We have left everything and followed you' *(Matt. 19: 27).* Jesus had replied that many people who had expected to find themselves first would be last, and those who thought they would be last would be first. He then told this story:

A man went out early one day to hire some labourers to work in his vineyard. He agreed with them to pay them each one silver coin per day, (which was a fair wage.)

At about nine o'clock he found men standing idle in the market-place and offered them work in his vineyard, agreeing to pay them a fair wage. He went out again about noon and again at about 3 o'clock and did the same thing.

Finally he went out at about 5 o'clock and found more men standing around doing nothing.

'Why are you idling about like this?' he asked. 'Because no-one has offered us work,' they replied. 'You can go and work in my vineyard,' he said, and the men went.

When evening came the man asked his foreman to go and call up all the workers so that they might receive their wages. When they arrived the man began paying them, starting with those whom he had taken on last. He gave them a silver coin each.

When the turn of those who had been taken on first came, they expected they would be given more, but each of them also received a silver coin as had been agreed when they had been taken on.

They began to grumble. 'Those men have only worked for one

hour and yet you have paid them the same as us, who have worked all day in the hot sunshine.'

The man answered, 'I have not cheated you. Did you not agree to work for a silver coin? If I wish to be generous to the others, then you must not begrudge me my kindness; am I not allowed to do as I wish with my own money?'

God does not owe anyone anything. Everything He gives us is an act of grace on His part. If the 'last' seem to get a similar reward to those who feel they should be 'first', then it is only so in the sight of those who expected more. It is their jealousy which makes them feel that others have had better treatment, and they must not grumble at God's generosity.

NOTES

Publican : This word in the New Testament refers to the tax collectors who collected taxes on behalf of the Roman Occupying Power. These men often cheated and collected more than they were entitled to, and so were hated and despised by the Jews. They also mixed with the Gentiles and were therefore regarded by the Jews as 'unclean'. Many people were surprised when Jesus spoke to and even ate with tax-collectors, but they had not learnt the lesson that Jesus despises no-one.

Prodigal : recklessly wasteful.

Talent : a sum of money, not usually a single coin. It was of high value and varied according to the weight of metal, gold or silver. It was probably worth about £350.